A LETTER TO THE WORLD

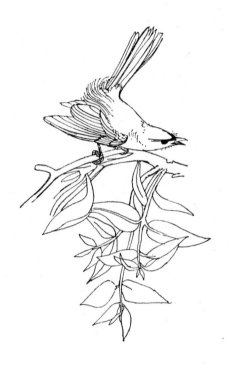

Emily Dickinson

A Letter
to the World

Poems for young readers
chosen and introduced by
Rumer Godden

DECORATED BY
Prudence Seward

THE MACMILLAN COMPANY

First published in Great Britain by The Bodley Head Ltd, 1968

Selection and introduction © Rumer Godden, 1968

Illustrations © The Bodley Head Ltd, 1968

Library of Congress catalog card number: 78-78083
Printed in the United States of America
First Printing

Introduction

Amherst, where Emily Dickinson lived her uneventful life, is a small and pleasant town in Massachusetts among rolling hills and valleys. It has a college—her grandfather was one of the founders; white frame houses and small shops are set around a green with an old inn, the Lord Jeffery. Main Street, where the Dickinson families lived, belies its name; it is wide, lined with trees and large houses in gardens of lilacs and snowball bushes. The Mansion, as Edward Dickinson's house was called—though it was no bigger than any of the others in the street—stands in an enclave with the Evergreens, that house "a hedge away" built for Emily's brother Austin; a secret path led from one house to the other.

"Who could have imagined," one of Amherst's summer visitors was to write after the first publication of the poems; "Who could have imagined . . . that, all unknown to the thousands that passed her house, there was a mind and imagination that could tell them more of nature and the mysteries of life than the combined wisdom of the College. They should have sensed," he said, "the presence of one who was reading the inner life of bee, grass and sky; the secret of the . . . lives of men and women." No one imagined. How could they? Though there are plenty of minor women poets and versifiers, those of real stature are so rare that,

7

counting down the centuries, they can be numbered on the fingers of one hand. Who, in Amherst, in the wholesome plain-living atmosphere of the nineteenth century, could have dreamed that Edward Dickinson's plain elder daughter Emily would turn out to be a major poet?

Edward Dickinson was a lawyer, a churchwarden of the Congregational Church and, as perhaps Amherst's most prominent citizen, was nicknamed "Squire" Dickinson. Emily, born in 1830, was one of three children, coming between Austin and a sister, Lavinia or Vinnie. "I have a brother and a sister," she wrote to Colonel Higginson, who became her friend, though not, as she had hoped, her mentor. "My mother does not care for thought and Father is too busy with his briefs to notice what we do. He buys me many books but begs me not to read them because he fears they joggle the mind." There was always a flick of dry humor in everything Emily wrote.

At school she was a wit, especially in writing valentines, and she often sent gay, small, in those days frequently sentimental notes and typically wry letters to her friends. As she grew up she went to all the functions of Amherst: evening parties and candlelight suppers; flower-picking excursions in the hills; in winter, "sugaring off" parties with bonfires in the snow. It was a happy normal life, but Emily had always been strangely independent and as time went on, people began to notice more and more, that "Emily was not there"; "not seen any more," until at forty, "I do not cross my father's ground to any house in town," she wrote to the Colonel. Nor, with very few exceptions, did anyone see her; she was, rather, a presence, hovering just out of sight as she listened to the piano being played or overheard a neighbor gossiping with Lavinia.

All kinds of reasons have been given for Emily Dickinson's seclusion; the favorite being that she was thwarted in love. We think of her so much as aloof, alone, that we forget there were many men in her life, of whom two, dear friends, died when she was very young; their deaths made an indelible impression—her poems about death are among her best. She was in love at least twice; first and passionately with the Reverend Charles Wadsworth, a Calvinist minister and powerful preacher. Mr. Wadsworth was married, and after their first acquaintance in Philadelphia, it seems Emily only saw him twice when he made two brief visits to the Mansion, twenty years apart. Even if Mr. Wadsworth had been free, would she have married him? Years later, when she and her father's friend, Judge Otis Phillips Lord, fell mutually in love, though he was a widower and there was no impediment, they did not marry. One guesses—and can only guess —that a spirit such as hers had to be free. Long before she met Mr. Wadsworth, Emily Dickinson had taken a solitary path. It is true that in her thirties she went through some crisis that brought what seems a crucible of suffering, with a growing apprehension—in both senses of the word—of the invisible forces round about us, which she faced with stoical wisdom, always keeping her poise. It certainly brought a surge of poetry; from 1860 onward Emily Dickinson's life and her poetry—one the echo of the other— totally engrossed her. "To live is so startling it leaves little time for anything else," she wrote.

One of the few people she did see was Colonel Higginson. He had written an article for the *Atlantic* magazine in which he encouraged young and new contributors. Emily Dickinson read it, found it echoed some of her ideas, and sent him a few of her poems with the cryptic sentence: "Are you too occupied to tell me if my verses are alive?" The Colonel could not deny it; though, to his conventional mind, they did not seem to be poetry, they were hauntingly alive, and letters went back and forth—until in 1870 he visited her. "I sent up my card. A parlor, dark and cool and stiffish. A step like a pattering child's in entry and in glided

9

a little plain woman with two smooth bands of reddish hair and a face with no good feature, in a very plain and exquisitely clean white piqué." (Emily Dickinson always wore white in her seclusion.) "She came to me with two day lilies which she put in a childish way into my hand and said, 'These are my introductions,' in a soft frightened breathless voice." To Emily the poet, her two lilies, or even one, had as much meaning as a bouquet but one cannot be surprised that the Colonel was bewildered. In a way, Emily Dickinson was naive and too easily believed that her friends saw what she saw, could share and understand. Usually they could not; they often found her notes, verses and letters baffling—yet mysteriously they kept them all their lives.

Colonel Higginson never knew what to make of her: "The bee did not evade the schoolboy more than she evaded me," he wrote, and defended himself by referring to "my partially cracked poetess at Amherst." Colonel Higginson was kindly but not particularly perceptive and did not understand that he was not dealing with a spinster poetess as he thought, but with an outstanding poet. He was kind but condescending, yet Colonel Higginson is only known today because Emily Dickinson singled him out.

The Colonel tried to tempt her to Boston, to join in the literary life there; Emily would have none of it. The only people she felt at ease with, found comradeship with, were children who were drawn, as by a magnet, to play in the grounds of the Mansion. To them, Miss Emily was a perfect playmate, though always on the fringe of their play. Sometimes, in the midst of a game of pirates or shipwrecked sailors, "a signal would be given, a soft tap on the glass of Miss Emily's window or a fluttered handkerchief, and the window would be opened silently and soon on the window ledge would appear a basket. It would be slowly lowered, two delicate hands playing out a much knotted cord. The basket always contained gingerbread—crisp and brown on the outside, within deliciously sweet and gummy." Emily was an excellent cook; she had won a prize with a loaf of her "rye and Indian bread."*

The boys and girls of course noticed that Miss Emily was apt to disappear suddenly. "My dears, if the butcher boy called, I should have to jump in the flour barrel," she told them. The children naturally hoped she would but they never asked why; they, like her family and neighbors, accepted that Miss Emily was "different"—but how different was only found out after her death.

Emily Dickinson died of an old illness when she was fifty-five, as quietly as she had lived; a neighbor's child who watched the funeral procession as it passed slowly through the blossoming fields—"while bluebirds and orioles were singing ecstatically and apple blossoms were filling the air with delicious odours"—remembered only how small the coffin was.* *

That child was Millicent Todd, daughter of Mrs. Loomis Todd who was to play such a large part in the publication of Emily Dickinson's work.

Six of Emily Dickinson's poems were printed in her lifetime—and were "robbed of her" as she wrote to Colonel Higginson because in every case the editors altered rhyme and phrase to make the poems fit current ideas of poetry; she had often sent verses, small poems, in notes and letters to relatives and friends—letters, to her, were a necessity—so that everyone who knew her, knew too that she wrote poetry, but no one had the slightest idea of its extent and caliber until, in the May after her death, Lavinia Dickinson, alone now in the big house, went into Emily's room— one guesses it still seemed to be inhabited—and, in the bottom drawer of the cherry-wood bureau, found a box full

* *Emily Dickinson, Friend and Neighbour*, MacGregor Jenkins, 1930.
* * *Ancestors' Brocades*, Millicent Todd Bingham, 1945.

of packets of poems. Each packet was made of small sheets of writing paper, threaded together to make small "volumes" as Vinnie called them. These alone held 879 poems; and, as time went on, more and more poems were discovered; altogether over seventeen hundred.

They were difficult to decipher, being written in three different and peculiar handwriting styles. Some were fair copies; some drafts or worksheets; most had crosses before several of the words, marking alternatives at the foot of the page, with no indication as to which was preferred. Each poem too, was strewn, it seemed almost haphazardly, with capitals and dashes.

The poems themselves were even more amazing than their looks; when they were deciphered it was clear there had been none like them before. They were not only original, they seemed too original and it was only through Vinnie's persistence that they were published at all. She took them first to the sister-in-law Sue, but though Sue kept the poems all winter, she did not, as she had promised, make clear copies. Vinnie then went to the child Millicent's mother, Mrs. Loomis Todd, a gifted and charming woman who used to come and play Bach and Scarlatti to an invisible Emily. Vinnie persuaded Mrs. Todd to decipher, copy and edit—with Colonel Higginson—a first selection of poems. Poor Mrs. Todd! She was to undergo years of hard labor but she was a devoted pioneer of Emily Dickinson.

In every way it was a difficult task. We, nowadays, are used to unusual idioms but even so, Emily Dickinson's seem strange; in 1890 they were startling. Poetry then was written in "poetical" style, exact in meter, thorough and logical in phrase, with exact rhymes; it was lofty and "beautiful" in thought. Then came this style like glancing light, the paradox of an odd flippancy about serious matters like death and God, with an immense awareness of their insoluble mystery. There was an unpretentious camaraderie.

"I'm Nobody! Who are you?
Are you—Nobody—too?"

(One wonders what would have happened had Emily
Dickinson said that to the important man of letters, Colonel
Higginson?) There was broken or "cut" meter, while the
rhymes were often incomplete and the use of words outland-
ish. "Otter window"? What did the poet mean?—one
guesses a built-in hidden window. "The mail from Tunis"
in "The Humming Bird"? Shakespeare's *The Tempest* might
have been the source:

"She that is queen of Tunis; she that dwells
Ten leagues beyond man's life; she that from Naples
Can have no note, unless the sun were post."

There are often echoes of Shakespeare in Emily Dickinson's poems, and then:

"The grass so little has to do
I wish I were a hay."

"It cannot go in, so," Colonel Higginson told Mrs. Todd.
"Everybody would say that 'hay' is a collective noun re-
quiring the definite article. Nobody can call it 'a hay.'"
Mrs. Todd protested that Emily did.

It seemed more and more perplexing—even ill-starred:
Colonel Higginson was "tepid," the publisher advised
against publishing, but Vinnie pushed on, though she had
to pay for the printing. When the book came out, the re-
ception at first was extraordinarily mixed: a few critics were
fascinated, more were later jerked into awareness, but many
sneered and most asked, as Colonel Higginson had asked,
"Is it poetry?" It is a pity that those shortsighted men could
not have taken a look into the future.

In that first small book there were only one hundred and

sixteen poems. It was bound in white with a drab back and, stamped in silver on the front, was a design of Indian pipes, those seemingly fragile resilient flowers that Mrs. Todd rightly thought might be a symbol of Emily. The book is now a collector's rare piece, and it was only the beginning. Two other books of poems followed—then a selection of letters—then selection after selection, collection after collection. Emily Dickinson's biography has been written and rewritten; there have been neighbors' books about her, memoirs, more letters, and several scholarly analyses of the poems; probably no poet living within the last century has such a bibliography. She has her own room now, in the Houghton Library at Harvard University, where her square piano, the minute desk at which she wrote those hundreds of poems, her amethyst seal, her watch with a key to wind it, are reverently kept. Amherst College houses most of her manuscripts in a priceless collection.

It seems a great fuss to make over such little poems, but are they little? Emily Dickinson's poems are the pith or essence of a completely original and perceptive mind and, like all distillations, they are potent: though they are short, it is not wise to read more than one or two of her poems at a time.

She has been compared to Blake or Emily Brontë, but these were great poets; Emily Dickinson is not "great," she is unique—and how few even of the great, are that? No one else has ever written like her and it is safe to predict no one will because she has a quicksilver quality, impossible to capture; but she has another importance for us—if she would have accepted such a thing as importance—she lived at "first hand," not secondhand as most of us do, not letting her days be ordered, or swallowed up, overlaid and cluttered by other people's thoughts as we, with our newspapers, radio, television, phonographs, paperbacks, advertisements, allow ourselves to be.

She knew the secret of savoring the world; knew that if we are to live at all, we must live in our "now," not looking back nostalgically into the past, nor straining forward to a future we hope will somehow be different, but living the present moment to the full. Her methods were her own—and would not do for us—but Emily Dickinson did not, as most people think, turn away from the world, she turned into it and found riches, as the poems disclose in every line.

> "This is my letter to the World
>   That never wrote to Me—
>   The simple news that Nature told—
>   With tender Majesty
>
>   Her Message is committed
>   To Hands I cannot see—
>   For love of Her—Sweet—countrymen—
>   Judge tenderly—of Me"

RUMER GODDEN

Contents

"To live is so startling it leaves little time
for anything else."
from a letter by
EMILY DICKINSON

[1]

This is my letter to the World
That never wrote to Me—
The simple news that Nature told—
With tender Majesty

Her Message is committed
To Hands I cannot see—
For love of Her—Sweet—countrymen—
Judge tenderly—of Me

I'll tell you how the Sun rose—
A Ribbon at a time—
The Steeples swam in Amethyst—
The news, like Squirrels, ran—

The Hills untied their Bonnets—
The Bobolinks—begun—
Then I said softly to myself—
" That must have been the Sun " !

But how he set—I know not—
There seemed a purple stile
That little Yellow boys and girls
Were climbing all the while—

Till when they reached the other side,
A Dominie in Gray—
Put gently up the evening Bars—
And led the flock away—

[3]

How still the Bells in Steeples stand
Till swollen with the Sky
They leap upon their silver Feet
In frantic Melody!

[4]

HUMMING BIRD

A Route of Evanescence
With a revolving Wheel—
A Resonance of Emerald—
A Rush of Cochineal—
And every Blossom on the Bush
Adjusts it's tumbled Head—
The mail from Tunis, probably,
An easy Morning's Ride—

The Way I read a Letter's—this—
'Tis first—I lock the Door—
And push it with my fingers—next—
For transport it be sure—

And then I go the furthest off
To counteract a knock—
Then draw my little Letter forth
And slowly pick the lock—

Then—glancing narrow, at the Wall—
And narrow at the floor
For firm Conviction of a Mouse
Not exorcised before—

Peruse how infinite I am
To no one that You—know—
And sigh for lack of Heaven—but not
The Heaven God bestow—

[6]

I'm Nobody! Who are you?
Are you—Nobody—too?
Then there's a pair of us!
Don't tell! they'd banish us—you know!

How dreary—to be—Somebody!
How public—like a Frog—
To tell your name—the livelong June—
To an admiring Bog!

[7]

There is no Frigate like a Book
To take us Lands away
Nor any Coursers like a Page
Of prancing Poetry—
This Travel may the poorest take
Without offence of Toll—
How frugal is the Chariot
That bears the Human soul.

I started Early—Took my Dog—
And visited the Sea—
The Mermaids in the Basement
Came out to look at me—

And Frigates—in the Upper Floor
Extended Hempen Hands—
Presuming Me to be a Mouse—
Aground—upon the Sands—

But no Man moved Me—till the Tide
Went past my simple Shoe—
And past my Apron—and my Belt
And past my Boddice—too—

And made as He would eat me up—
As wholly as a Dew
Upon a Dandelion's Sleeve—
And then—I started—too—

And He—He followed—close behind—
I felt His Silver Heel
Upon my Ancle—Then my Shoes
Would overflow with Pearl—

Until We met the Solid Town—
No One He seemed to know—
And bowing—with a Mighty look—
At me—The Sea withdrew—

Through lane it lay—thro' bramble—
Through clearing and thro' wood—
Banditti often passed us
Upon the lonely road.

The wolf came peering curious—
The owl looked puzzled down—
The serpent's satin figure
Glid stealthily along—

The tempests touched our garments—
The lightning's poinards gleamed—
Fierce from the Crag above us
The hungry Vulture screamed—

The satyrs fingers beckoned—
The valley murmured "Come"—
These were the mates—
This was the road
These children fluttered home.

[10]

A narrow Fellow in the Grass
Occasionally rides—
You may have met Him—did you not
His notice sudden is—

The Grass divides as with a Comb—
A spotted shaft is seen—
And then it closes at your feet
And opens further on—

He likes a Boggy Acre
A Floor too cool for Corn—
Yet when a Boy, and Barefoot—
I more than once at Noon
Have passed, I thought, a Whip lash
Unbraiding in the Sun
When stooping to secure it
It wrinkled, and was gone—

Several of Nature's People
I know, and they know me—
I feel for them a transport
Of cordiality—

But never met this Fellow
Attended, or alone
Without a tighter breathing
And Zero at the Bone—

A Thought went up my mind today—
That I have had before—
But did not finish—some way back—
I could not fix the Year—

Nor where it went—nor why it came
The second time to me—
Nor definitely, what it was—
Have I the Art to say—

But somewhere—in my Soul—I know—
I've met the Thing before—
It just reminded me—'twas all—
And came my way no more—

The Brain—is wider than the Sky—
For—put them side by side—
The one the other will contain
With ease—and You—beside—

The Brain is deeper than the sea—
For—hold them—Blue to Blue—
The one the other will absorb—
As Sponges—Buckets—do—

The Brain is just the weight of God—
For—Heft them—Pound for Pound—
And they will differ—if they do—
As Syllable from Sound—

[13]

(an extract)

The Skies cant keep their secret!
They tell it to the Hills—
The Hills just tell the Orchards—
And they—the Daffodils!

A Bird—by chance—that goes that way—
Soft overhears the whole—
If I should bribe the little Bird—
Who knows but *she* would tell?

[14]

An altered look about the hills—
A Tyrian light the village fills—
A wider sunrise in the morn—
A deeper twilight on the lawn—
A print of a vermillion foot—
A purple finger on the slope—
A flippant fly upon the pane—
A spider at his trade again—
An added strut in Chanticleer—
A flower expected everywhere—
An axe shrill singing in the woods—
Fern odors on untravelled roads—
All this and more I cannot tell—
A furtive look you know as well—
And Nicodemus' Mystery
Receives it's annual reply!

"Nicodemus saith unto him, How can a man be born when
he is old? can he enter the second time into his mother's
womb, and be born?"

John, III, 4

I like to see it lap the Miles—
And lick the Valleys up—
And stop to feed itself at Tanks—
And then—prodigious step

Around a Pile of Mountains—
And supercilious peer
In Shanties—by the sides of Roads—
And then a Quarry pare

To fit it's sides
And crawl between
Complaining all the while
In horrid—hooting stanza—
Then chase itself down Hill—

And neigh like Boanerges—
Then—prompter than a Star
Stop—docile and omnipotent
At it's own stable door—

How soft a Caterpillar steps—
I find one on my Hand
From such a velvet world it comes
Such plushes at command
It's soundless travels just arrest
My slow—terrestrial eye
Intent upon it's own career
What use has it for me—

The Soul selects her own Society—
Then—shuts the Door—
To her divine Majority—
Present no more—

Unmoved—she notes the Chariots—pausing—
At her low Gate—
Unmoved—an Emperor be kneeling
Upon her Mat—

I've known her—from an ample nation—
Choose One—
Then—close the Valves of her attention—
Like Stone—

I held a Jewel in my fingers—
And went to sleep—
The day was warm, and winds were prosy—
I said "'Twill keep"—

I woke—and chid my honest fingers,
The Gem was gone—
And now, an Amethyst remembrance
Is all I own—

I never lost as much but twice,
And that was in the sod.
Twice have I stood a beggar
Before the door of God!

Angels—twice descending
Reimbursed my store—
Burglar! Banker—Father!
I am poor once more!

[20]

(an extract)

Who never wanted—maddest Joy
Remains to him unknown—
The Banquet of Abstemiousness
Surpasses that of Wine—

[21]

I taste a liquor never brewed—
From Tankards scooped in Pearl—
Not all the Frankfort Berries
Yield such an Alcohol!

Inebriate of Air—am I—
And Debauchee of Dew—
Reeling—thro endless summer days—
From inns of Molten Blue—

When "Landlords" turn the drunken Bee
Out of the Foxglove's door—
When Butterflies—renounce their "drams"—
I shall but drink the more!

Till Seraphs swing their snowy Hats—
And Saints—to windows run—
To see the little Tippler
Leaning against the—Sun—

I never hear the word "escape"
Without a quicker blood,
A sudden expectation,
A flying attitude!

I never hear of prisons broad
By soldiers battered down,
But I tug childish at my bars
Only to fail again!

"Hope" is the thing with feathers—
That perches in the soul—
And sings the tune without the words—
And never stops—at all—

And sweetest—in the Gale—is heard—
And sore must be the storm—
That could abash the little Bird
That kept so many warm—

I've heard it in the chillest land—
And on the strangest Sea—
Yet, never, in Extremity,
It asked a crumb—of Me.

When I hoped, I recollect
Just the place I stood—
At a Window facing West—
Roughest Air—was good—

Not a Sleet could bite me—
Not a frost could cool—
Hope it was that kept me warm—
Not Merino shawl—

When I feared—I recollect
Just the Day it was—
Worlds were lying out to Sun—
Yet how Nature froze—

Icicles upon my soul
Prickled Blue and Cool—
Bird went praising everywhere—
Only Me—was still—

And the Day that I despaired—
This—if I forget
Nature will—that it be Night
After Sun has set—
Darkness intersect her face—
And put out her eye—
Nature hesitate—before
Memory and I—

A Bird came down the Walk—
He did not know I saw—
He bit an Angleworm in halves
And ate the fellow, raw,

And then he drank a Dew
From a convenient Grass—
And then hopped sidewise to the Wall
To let a Beetle pass—

He glanced with rapid eyes
That hurried all around—
They looked like frightened Beads, I thought—
He stirred his Velvet Head

Like one in danger, Cautious,
I offered him a Crumb
And he unrolled his feathers
And rowed him softer home—

Than Oars divide the Ocean,
Too silver for a seam—
Or Butterflies, off Banks of Noon
Leap, plashless as they swim.

A soft Sea washed around the House
A Sea of Summer Air
And rose and fell the magic Planks
That sailed without a care—
For Captain was the Butterfly
For Helmsman was the Bee
And an entire universe
For the delighted crew.

The Wind begun to rock the Grass
With threatening Tunes and low—
He threw a Menace at the Earth—
A Menace at the Sky.

The Leaves unhooked themselves from Trees—
And started all abroad
The Dust did scoop itself like Hands
And threw away the Road.

The Wagons quickened on the Streets
The Thunder hurried slow—
The Lightning showed a Yellow Beak
And then a livid Claw.

The Birds put up the Bars to Nests—
The Cattle fled to Barns—
There came one drop of Giant Rain
And then as if the Hands

That held the Dams had parted hold
The Waters Wrecked the Sky,
But overlooked my Father's House—
Just quartering a Tree—

I felt a Cleaving in my Mind—
As if my Brain had split—
I tried to match it—Seam by Seam—
But could not make them fit.

The thought behind, I strove to join
Unto the thought before—
But Sequence ravelled out of Sound
Like Balls—upon a Floor.

After great pain, a formal feeling comes—
The Nerves sit ceremonious, like Tombs—
The stiff Heart questions was it He, that bore,
And Yesterday, or Centuries before?

The Feet, mechanical, go round—
Of Ground, or Air, or Ought—
A Wooden way
Regardless grown,
A Quartz contentment, like a stone—

This is the Hour of Lead—
Remembered, if outlived,
As Freezing persons, recollect the Snow—
First—Chill—then Stupor—then the letting go—

Our lives are Swiss—
So still—so Cool—
Till some odd afternoon
The Alps neglect their Curtains
And we look farther on!

Italy stands the other side!
While like a guard between—
The solemn Alps—
The siren Alps
Forever intervene!

The Spider holds a Silver Ball
In unperceived Hands—
And dancing softly to Himself
His Yarn of Pearl—unwinds—

He plies from Nought to Nought—
In unsubstantial Trade—
Supplants our Tapestries with His—
In half the period—

An Hour to rear supreme
His Continents of Light—
Then dangle from the Housewife's Broom—
His Boundaries—forgot—

Because I could not stop for Death—
He kindly stopped for me—
The Carriage held but just Ourselves—
And Immortality.

We slowly drove—He knew no haste
And I had put away
My labor and my leisure too,
For His Civility—

We passed the School, where Children strove
At Recess—in the Ring—
We passed the Fields of Gazing Grain—
We passed the Setting Sun—

Or rather—He passed Us—
The Dews drew quivering and chill—
For only Gossamer, my Gown—
My Tippet—only Tulle—

We paused before a House that seemed
A Swelling of the Ground—
The Roof was scarcely visible—
The Cornice—in the Ground—

Since then—'tis Centuries—and yet
Feels shorter than the Day
I first surmised the Horses Heads
Were toward Eternity—

Our journey had advanced—
Our feet were almost come
To that odd Fork in Being's Road—
Eternity—by Term—

Our pace took sudden awe—
Our feet—reluctant—led—
Before—were Cities—but Between—
The Forest of the Dead—

Retreat—was out of Hope—
Behind—a Sealed Route—
Eternity's White Flag—Before—
And God—at every Gate—

I never saw a Moor—
I never saw the Sea—
Yet know I how the Heather looks
And what a Billow be.

I never spoke with God
Nor visited in Heaven—
Yet certain am I of the spot
As if the Checks were given—

Tho' I get home how late—how late—
So I get home—'twill compensate—
Better will be the Extasy
That they have done expecting me—
When Night—descending—dumb—and dark—
They hear my unexpected knock—
Transporting must the moment be—
Brewed from decades of Agony!

To think just how the fire will burn—
Just how long-cheated eyes will turn—
To wonder what myself will say,
And what itself, will say to me—
Beguiles the Centuries of way!

This quiet Dust was Gentlemen and Ladies
And Lads and Girls—
Was laughter and ability and Sighing
And Frocks and Curls.

This Passive Place a Summer's nimble mansion
Where Bloom and Bees
Exist an Oriental Circuit
Then cease, like these—

Safe in their Alabaster Chambers—
Untouched by Morning
And untouched by Noon—
Sleep the meek members of the Resurrection—
Rafter of satin,
And Roof of stone.

Light laughs the breeze
In her Castle above them—
Babbles the Bee in a stolid Ear,
Pipe the Sweet Birds in ignorant cadence—
Ah, what sagacity perished here!

PINE BOUGH

A feather from the Whippowil
That everlasting—sings!
Whose galleries—are Sunrise—
Whose Opera—the Springs—
Whose Emerald Nest the Ages spin
Of mellow—murmuring thread—
Whose Beryl Egg, what School Boys hunt
In "Recess"—Overhead!

The morns are meeker than they were—
The nuts are getting brown—
The berry's cheek is plumper—
The Rose is out of town.

The Maple wears a gayer scarf—
The field a scarlet gown—
Lest I sh'd be old fashioned
I'll put a trinket on.

[40]

A Saucer holds a Cup
In sordid human Life
But in a Squirrel's estimate
A Saucer holds a Loaf.

A Table of a Tree
Demands the little King
And every Breeze that run along
His Dining Room do swing.

His Cutlery—he keeps
Without his Russet Lips—
To see it flashing when he dines
Do Birmingham eclipse—

Convicted—could we be
Of our Minutiae
The smallest Citizen that flies
Is heartier than we—

Presentiment—is that long Shadow—on the Lawn—
Indicative that Suns go down—

The Notice to the startled Grass
That Darkness—is about to pass—

I know some lonely Houses off the Road
A Robber'd like the look of—
Wooden barred,
And Windows hanging low,
Inviting to—
A Portico,
Where two could creep—
One—hand the Tools—
The other peep—
To make sure All's Asleep—
Old fashioned eyes—
Not easy to surprise!

How orderly the Kitchen'd look, by night,
With just a Clock—
But they could gag the Tick—
And Mice wont bark—
And so the Walls—dont tell—
None—will—

A pair of Spectacles ajar just stir—
An Almanac's aware—
Was it the Mat—winked,
Or a Nervous Star?
The Moon—slides down the stair,
To see who's there!

There's plunder—where—
Tankard, or Spoon—
Earring—or Stone—
A Watch—Some Ancient Brooch
To match the Grandmama—
Staid sleeping—there—

Day—rattles—too
Stealth's—slow—
The Sun has got as far
As the third Sycamore—
Screams Chanticleer,
"Who's there"?

And Echoes—Trains away,
Sneer—"Where"!
While the old Couple, just astir,
Fancy the Sunrise—left the door ajar!

Blazing in Gold and quenching in Purple
Leaping like Leopards to the Sky
Then at the feet of the old Horizon
Laying her spotted Face to die
Stooping as low as the Otter's Window
Touching the Roof and tinting the Barn
Kissing her Bonnet to the Meadow
And the Juggler of Day is gone

She sweeps with many-colored Brooms—
And leaves the Shreds behind—
Oh Housewife in the Evening West—
Come back, and dust the Pond!

You dropped a Purple Ravelling in—
You dropped an Amber thread—
And now you've littered all the East
With Duds of Emerald!

And still, she plies her spotted Brooms,
And still the Aprons fly,
Till Brooms fade softly into stars—
And then I come away—

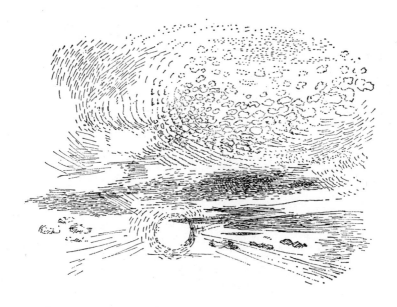

Index of First Lines

WITHDRAWN